CW00418989

BUTTERFLIES
OF THE CAPE PENINSULA
A comprehensive guide

A.J.M. Claassens

DEDICATION

I affectionately dedicate this work to my wife Jill and our granddaughters, Tessa, Julia, Claudia and Georgia.

Tafelberg Publishers

First published 2000 by Tafelberg Publishers
Wale Street, Cape Town, South Africa

Registration number: 51/02378/06

Copyright © published edition: Tafelberg Publishers
Copyright © text: A.J.M. Claassens
Copyright © photographs: A.J.M. Claassens, with the exception of those listed below
Copyright © line illustrations: S. F. Henning
Copyright © map: E. B. Hofer

Photographic credits: Alan Heath: 16c, 23d, 25c, 25d, 26d, 27c, 27d, 28c, 28d, 29c, 30d, 31c, 31d, 32c, 33c, representing one or more early stages of 11 ant-associated lycaenids.

10 9 8 7 6 5 4 3 2 1

Publisher Dick Wilkins
Editor Brenda Brickman
Designer Mandy McKay
Production manager Andrew de Kock
Reproduction by Unifoto (Pty) Ltd, Cape Town
Printed and bound by Tien Wah Press (Pte) Ltd, Singapore

All rights reserved. No part of this publication may be reproduced, stored in a retrieval system or transmitted, in any form or by any means, electronic, mechanical, photocopying, recording or otherwise, without the prior written permission of the copyright owner(s).

ISBN 0–624–038955

CONTENTS

INTRODUCTION

In their book, *Butterflies of the Table Mountain Range* (1980), the authors Claassens and Dickson dealt with the 53 species of butterfly then known to occur on this Peninsula range. This work is an extension of that guide, illustrating and comprehensively discussing the 70 species of ıtterfly presently known to occur in the entire Cape Peninsula.

Twenty or so Peninsula butterflies are common garden and roadside butterflies, but most s· ᴄies are localised and often rare mountain and coastal Fynbos insects. Some of the Peninsula ᴧtterflies are threatened with extinction and others have disappeared from previously known ıocalities, although some of these may still thrive elsewhere. New, permanent arrivals have also been recorded in the area over the past two decades, and three occasional migrants from the eastern districts of the country visit the Cape Peninsula at irregular intervals.

About this book

In this work, the Cape Peninsula's butterflies are grouped under the families or subfamilies to which they belong. Numbering is sequential, and not taxonomically related, and, to facilitate ease of reference, the species in this book have been numbered from 1 to 70. Each time a butterfly is mentioned in this text, its common name is followed by the corresponding number.

The uppersides of the butterflies, most often of both male and female, as well as the underside of either the male or female of every species is depicted in colour, as is one or more of the early stages of many species. Informative details regarding size, distribution, flight period, larval food and early stages are offered alongside the corresponding plates. In some species, additional notes have been added to highlight features or habits of particular interest and, in the introductory text, a few line illustrations have been added to enhance understanding of the relevant text. In the so-called Blues and Coppers, special attention is devoted to the association of their larvae with ants.

Vernacular and scientific names

This guide is aimed at the lay person with a general interest in the flora and fauna of the Cape Peninsula. With that in mind, the common (vernacular) names of the butterflies and ants with which the larvae of many species are associated, are used throughout the text. Of the larval food plants too, common names, where these are known, are used. A number of butterflies have more than one common name, but only those names which are most appropriate for the Peninsula species are used in this work. The scientific names of butterflies and their food plants and host ants are also provided, as are the common Afrikaans butterfly names.

Cape Peninsula inland boundary

For the purposes of this book, the inland boundary of the Cape Peninsula is regarded to be represented by a straight line drawn from the Milnerton Lighthouse on the West Coast of the Peninsula, to Strandfontein on the East Coast, encompassing the Cape Peninsula National Park. However, a few butterflies, including the Sand-dune Widow (6), Feltham's Opal (29), Barber's Ranger (63), Unique Ranger (64), White-branded Swift (66), and perhaps Silver Arrowhead (18), are almost entirely restricted to the low-lying areas bordering the Cape Flats.

Butterfly wealth of the Cape Peninsula

Of the more than 650 species of butterfly known to occur in South Africa, the Western Cape boasts 150 varieties, and the Cape Peninsula is blessed with 67 species and subspecies, as well as three occasional migrants. For its size of less than 420 square kilometres, the Cape Peninsula has a rich butterfly fauna. However, the butterfly fauna of the Peninsula compares poorly with the extreme richness of its flora, and comparatively few plant families serve as food for butterfly larvae.

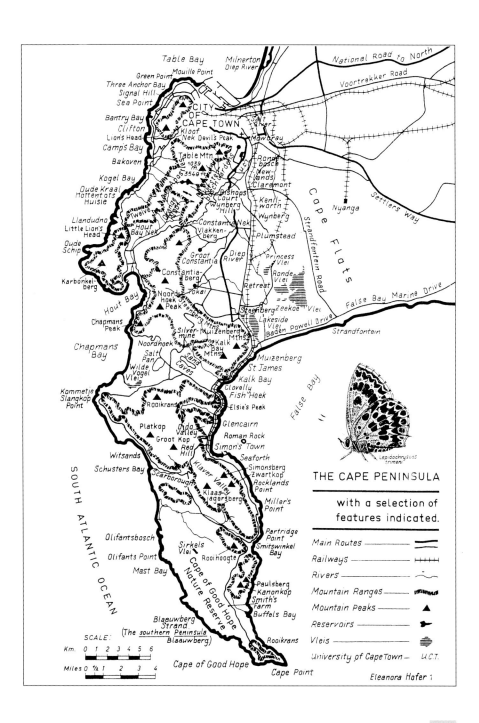

THE CAPE PENINSULA

with a selection of
features indicated.

Main Routes
Railways
Rivers
Mountain Ranges
Mountain Peaks
Reservoirs
Vleis
University of Cape Town — U.C.T.

Eleanora Hofer

Butterfly gains and losses

The African Migrant (54), the Common Dotted Border (52) and the Palm-tree Nightfighter (65) are recent arrivals in the Peninsula from the eastern districts of the country.

Moreover, the European Cabbage White (50) settled in the Peninsula as recently as 1994, and has spread into neighbouring areas. On the other hand, several species, once established in the Peninsula, have become rare, and some may have disappeared from the Fairest Cape altogether, probably never to return.

The disappearance of several species of plant from the Cape Peninsula, or even from Table Mountain, Signal Hill or Lion's Head, is a sad loss. Likewise the near disappearance of the Dark Opal (28), a butterfly of exquisite beauty, from Table Mountain, the disappearance of the pretty Protea Scarlet (17) from Signal Hill and Lion's Head, and the loss of the Jitterbug Daisy Copper (31), as well as the White-branded Swift (66) from Blinkwater Gorge and other erstwhile localities of these species and others on the Table Mountain range, are most regrettable.

The greatest threat to butterflies and animals in general is fragmentation and reduction of indigenous vegetation by urban expansion, invasion of alien plants and veld fires. All these factors and others affect the flora and fauna of the Cape Peninsula and will, of necessity, lead to loss of indigenous plants as well as butterflies and other animals.

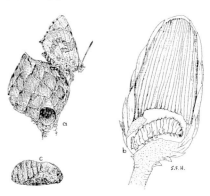

Fig. 1: The Protea Scarlet (17), a butterfly threatened by repeated veld fires. (a) Male on a Protea head. Note the exit hole through which the mature butterfly has emerged. (b) Section through a Protea head showing a Protea Scarlet larva feeding on the reproductive flower parts. (c) Pupa of the Protea Scarlet as found in a Protea head.

Association with ants (Myrmecophily)

Many butterflies, especially in their early stages, are not easily noticed unless searched for in their favourite haunts. This applies particularly to many Blues and Coppers, the larvae of which have a close association with certain ants. Ant association has been particularly well researched in the early stages of many Blues and Coppers occurring in the Peninsula, and is referred to in general under Blues and Coppers (pp. 9–10), and more specifically under each species in which it occurs. However, much research remains to be done.

Ants themselves are negatively affected not only by the destructive factors mentioned earlier. They are also threatened by the introduction of Argentine Ants, which have been known to destroy colonies of indigenous ants, including the Pugnacious Ant, the Small Black Sugar Ant, and the Brown House Ant, all of which, to varying degrees, are associated with Lycaenid larvae. All of these ants and other indigenous ants are also important Fynbos seed dispersers. These small ants even attack the much larger Spotted Sugar and Marsh Ants, which are essential hosts to the larvae of four Peninsula Blues (46, 47, 48, 49). They also attack and kill the Black Mound Termite and occupy their nests.

The Argentine Ant seems, perhaps due to its fresh water requirements, to favour areas fairly close to human habitations, and they do not appear to survive at high altitudes. Ant poisons used to control ants in homes and gardens may well be responsible for the ant becoming seemingly less common in residential areas.

Fig. 2: A papery shelter constructed by Cocktail Ants on a leaf of Bitou for a larva of the Water Opal (30).

Veld fires

Veld fires, when occurring in the same area in quick succession, are a threat to all living creatures, and may well have been a major factor in the disappearance or near disappearance of, among others, the now endangered Scarce Mountain Copper (19) from Lion's Head, the only known remaining habitat of this once more widely spread butterfly. It is, however, feared that this butterfly may have disappeared from this area and could well be heading for extinction even before its ant-associated life cycle has been unravelled. Fortunately, three subspecies of this insect occur elsewhere in the Western Cape. Veld fires coinciding with the main flight period of localised butterflies are most dangerous to the populations concerned as they destroy the butterflies and their eggs, their larvae and their food plants. However, the larvae and pupae of those Blues and Coppers that shelter in underground ants' nests, or in ants' nests under stones, are safeguarded against the effect of occasional fires. This is particularly true of non-plant-eating (aphytophagous) larvae, which feed on the host ants' brood or are fed by their host ants, and thus never vacate their places of safety until they emerge from them as adult butterflies. However, periodic or 'natural' veld fires occurring seven or more years apart improve Fynbos by destroying dominant, often alien vegetation, and allowing less vigorous and essential food plant species to re-establish themselves. For this reason, controlled fires are sometimes used to improve the chances of survival of rare and endangered species of plants and animals, including butterflies, in national parks and reserves.

Alien vegetation

Although the Nature Conservation authorities and other organisations continuously combat alien vegetation that threatens the unique flora of the Cape Peninsula, the battle is never won. Large areas of coastal and montane Fynbos, stretching from the Cape Flats to Cape Point, tend to become invaded by these 'green cancers'. The most common invaders are several species of *Acacia*, including Rooikrans, Wattle and Port Jackson. Other well-known invader species are Hackea, Cluster Pine and Stone Pine. Apart from being serious fire hazards, plant invaders kill indigenous plants, robbing them of light, water, soil nutrients and space. They also disturb indigenous fauna, often endemic to small regions to which their food or host plants are restricted. Butterflies and certain other insects imbibe nectar of indigenous flowers and in their early stages subsist on the leaves of these plants. Destruction of the natural food sources of herbivorous (phytophagous) invertebrates in turn affects the food chain involving invertebrate and vertebrate predators. Admittedly, the flowers of invader plants are visited by some adult insects, including bees and butterflies, while the larvae of many moths and some butterflies, including the Common Hairtail (45) feed on the leaves or flower buds of some without, however, becoming dependent on them for their survival. Exotic invaders can thus become alternative food plants of indigenous insects. The same is true of many introduced garden plants.

BUTTERFLY FAMILIES REPRESENTED IN THE CAPE PENINSULA

1 Nymphalids (with four subfamilies)

A Monarchs (Danaines) (1)

The Monarchs are a small group of fairly large, showy butterflies. They are unpalatable to vertebrate predators such as birds, lizards and snakes. They 'advertise' their distastefulness by means of their leisurely flight, brandishing the warning colours (orange-brown, white and black) of their wings.

Unrelated butterflies, palatable themselves, have, through a remarkable process of evolution, imitated the flaunting colours and lazy flight of the Monarchs and thus, sailing under false colours, have safeguarded themselves against potential predators that mistake them for their poisonous models. Their larvae and pupae are, however, often attacked and killed by parasitoids.

The only Monarch butterfly that occurs in the Cape Peninsula is the African Monarch (1), or Milkweed Butterfly.

B Browns (Satyrines) (2–12)

The Browns are a large group of mainly sombre-coloured, light to dark brown butterflies. They are mostly of a small to medium size. Their wings are often adorned with yellow, orange or red spots, as well as eyespots. These 'devices' are aimed at discouraging vertebrate predators from attacking them, or to direct their attacks on the wings, away from their more vulnerable heads or abdomens. Their underside colours and patterns camouflage the Browns when they are at rest with their wings closed.

Their larvae are mainly grass feeders and many of them, therefore, pass the dry summer months in a state of dormancy (estivation) to avoid starvation.

The following 11 species occur in the Cape Peninsula: Table Mountain Beauty (2), Cape Autumn Widow (3), Mintha Widow (4), Cape Spring Widow (5), Sand-dune Widow (6), Trimen's Brown (7), Silver-bottom Brown (8), Burchell's Brown (9), Western Hillside Brown (10), Rainforest Brown (11), and Boland Brown (12).

C Acraeas (Acraeines) (13)

The Acraeas are mostly bright red to carmine, medium-sized butterflies, often with partly transparent wings. They are distasteful to insectivorous predators such as birds and reptiles, which are warned by their bright colours and leisurely flight.

Their immunity to attacks by potential predators is enhanced by their unusually tough skin, which renders them difficult to crush. Unrelated species, some palatable but others unpalatable, have mimicked the colours, patterns and tauntingly slow flight of certain Acraeas to free them from predation. However, the larvae and pupae of the Acraeas are heavily parasitised, and their numbers are thus effectively controlled.

After mating the female Acraea develops a structure at the tip of her abdomen known as sphragis, which may serve to prevent subsequent matings by other males.

Although the Acraeas are represented by more than 40 species in southern Africa, only one species, the Garden Acraea (13), occurs in the Cape Peninsula.

D Nymphs (Nymphalines) (14)

Most Nymphs are robust, large- to medium-sized, colourful butterflies. Many Nymphs are indeed strikingly beautiful insects. They have a strong flight and often settle in open spaces, sunning themselves with outstretched wings.

Although well represented in southern Africa, including a number of common species, in the Cape Peninsula only one species, the Painted Lady (14), occurs.

Another two Nymphs, the Yellow Pansy (68) and the Common Diadem (69) reach the Peninsula occasionally as migrants.

2 Blues and Coppers (Lycaenids) (15–49)

The Blues and Coppers are a very large family of butterflies of varying sizes and colours. Half of the Cape Peninsula's butterflies belong to this family. Many Blues and Coppers are of exquisite beauty, and they are often attractively coloured and patterned even on the underside of their wings, which helps them to blend in with their immediate surroundings when resting with their wings closed.

Many of them possess delicate 'tails', often associated with eyespots, on their hindwings. When such a tailed species is settles with its wings closed and its head facing downwards, its posterior end resembles a butterfly head with eyes and antennae, at least when seen through the eyes of a bird or reptile. A predator striking at the false 'head' of a Lycaenid butterfly may come away with part of its wings, but without damaging its vital parts.

Fig. 3: The Common Blue bears hair-tails on its hindwings to represent a false head.

Ant association

The larvae of many Blues and Coppers are associated with certain ants, and for that purpose are structurally and behaviourally adapted. Many possess a honey gland, also known as a dorsal nectar organ, which is situated dorsally on the 7th abdominal segment of many Lycaenid larvae. This gland secretes a sweet substance, which is eagerly imbibed by sweet-loving ants. The general function of the honey gland is to appease the ants when they meet such larvae, and it assures the presence of the ants while the larvae are resting or feeding, so that they may be protected against attacks by parasitic wasps and flies during the day.

Fig. 4: A sweet-loving ant probing the honey gland of a Lycaenid larva with its antennae before imbibing the gland's secretion.

Tiny glands and other structures on Lycaenid larvae produce chemical substances that imitate the chemical messenger substances (pheremones) that are secreted by the ants themselves, and which make communication between the host ants and the larvae possible. Also important in ant association are a pair of retractile tubercles, or tentacle organs, present on the 8th abdominal segment of many Lycaenid larvae.

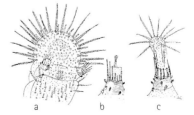

Fig. 5. Retractile tubercles (tentacle organs) of the Red Copper (20). (Highly magnified.)

(a) Terminal segments of a final instar larva showing the tubercles on the 8th abdominal segment.
(b) A tubercle partly extended from its casing.
(c) A fully extended tubercle with its hair-like processes. The Red Copper larva does not possess a honey gland in the final instar.

Details of these structures and their functions fall beyond the scope of this book. There are varying degrees of association between ants and Lycaenid larvae. Some have a very casual relationship, which is not essential for their survival. In others the association with ants is more intimate, and hence more important to the wellbeing of the larvae. There are also Lycaenid larvae that are totally dependent on their host ants and live in their nests at least for part of their larval stage, during which they cannot survive without them. Under the discussions of the various Blues and Coppers occurring in the Cape Peninsula, reference is made to the kind of association that exists between their larvae and their host ants.

Pupae of many Blues and Coppers are also visited by the ants with which they were associated during the larval stage. The ants appear to imbibe a secretion produced by tiny glands in the pupal skin. The removal of this secretion from the pupal skin seems to be beneficial to the pupae because it is difficult to rear adult butterflies from pupae collected from ants' nests. However, the microclimate prevailing in the host ants' nests may also contribute to the ability of the pupae to successfully complete their metamorphosis into adult butterflies.

The following 35 species of Blues and Coppers occur in the Cape Peninsula: Boland Skolly (15), Peninsula Skolly (16), Protea Scarlet (17), Silver Arrowhead (18), Scarce Mountain Copper* (19), Red Copper (20), Aranda Copper (21), Almeida Copper (22), Dull Copper (23), Red Hill Copper* (24), Burnished Copper (25), Common Opal (26), Sand-dune Opal (27), Dark Opal* (28), Feltham's Opal (29), Water Opal (30), Jitterbug Daisy Copper (31), Donkey Daisy Copper (32), Vivid Blue (33), Cupreous Blue (34), Lucerne Blue (35), Common Blue (36), Short-toothed Blue (37), Bush Blue (38), Common Geranium Bronze (39), Dickson's Geranium Bronze (40), Water Bronze (41), Sooty Blue (42), Western Sorrel Copper (43), Cape Black-eye (44), Common Hairtail (45), Monkey Blue (46), Trimen's Blue (47), Peninsula Blue (48), Robertson Blue (49).

Rare and endangered Lycaenids

Because of their very special life cycle requirements a large number of the South African Blues and Coppers are rare. Their habitats are often threatened by fire, encroachment of alien plants, and not least by human beings. The individual status of each of the affected Lycaenids is dealt with in the *Red Data Book of South African Butterflies* (Henning and Henning, 1989). Five of the Cape's Lycaenid butterflies are listed herein, and three of these (marked with an * above) are protected by law.

3 Whites and Yellows (Pierids) (50-54)

The Pierids or Whites and Yellows are a fairly large family of which 56 species and a number of subspecies occur in southern Africa. Many Pierids are attractive butterflies, especially those in which the tips of the forewings are a beautiful orange, red or purple in colour.

Until fairly recently only two species of Pierids occurred in the Cape Peninsula, but the Common Dotted Border (52) and the African Migrant (54) now also breed in the Peninsula, and since 1994 the European Large White, in this work referred to as the Cabbage White (50) after establishing itself in the Cape Peninsula, soon spread to adjacent territories.

The following species occur in the Cape Peninsula: Cabbage White (50), Meadow White (51), Common Dotted Border (52), African Clouded Yellow (53) and African Migrant (54).

4 Swallowtails and Swordtails (Papilionids) (55)

This family of mainly large butterflies is represented in southern Africa by seven Swallowtails and 10 Swordtails, or Kites. Only one species occurs in the Cape Peninsula, namely the Christmas Butterfly, or Citrus Swallowtail (55). Ironically this species is tailless. Another tailless species, the handsome Green-banded Swallowtail, has been recorded once or twice as a migrant from the Peninsula. However, the closest its known distribution approaches the Peninsula is in Swellendam, where it appears to have established itself well in Citrus orchards. The larvae of the Pipilionids possess a forked protrusible organ, called the osmeterium, situated behind the head. When disturbed the larva bends its anterior end towards the attacker and the osmeterium is shot out, releasing a repulsive acrid smell, which results in the quick retreat of the attacker.

Papilionid larvae are distasteful to vertebrate predators such as lizards, snakes and birds, although the Fiscal Shrike *(Lanius collaris)* has been seen to prey on the final instar larvae of the Citrus Swallowtail (55).

5 Skippers (Hesperids) (56-67)

The Skippers are mostly sombre-, drab-coloured insects with a rapid, often skipping or jumpy flight. They constitute a large family with more than 120 species occurring in southern Africa.

Most Skippers are day-flying, but some species are crepuscular and are sometimes attracted to artificial light. Regarded by some scientists as the most primitive of butterflies, they are classified as a transitional group between butterflies and moths as they have certain characteristics of both kinds of insects in common. They are small to medium-sized butterflies.

The following 12 species occur in the Cape Peninsula: Dwarf Sandman (56), Boland Sandman (57), Common Sandman (58), Mafa Sandman (59), Mountain Sandman (60), Grassveld Sylph (61), Gold-spotted Sylph (62), Barber's Ranger (63), Unique Ranger (64), Palmtree Nightfighter (65), White-branded Swift (66), Common Hottentot (67).

6 Occasional migrants (68-70)

From time to time, possibly due to population explosions resulting in an acute shortage of larval food plants in their natural habitats, a number of butterflies migrate.

Occasionally, usually in late summer or autumn, some of these migrants reach the Cape Peninsula. Migrants most likely to be seen here are the Yellow Pansy (68), the Common Diadem (69) and the Brown-veined White (70).

The Brown-veined White ♂ photographed in Sea Point in 1980

Monarchs (Danaines)

1 African Monarch *Danaus chrysippus aegyptius* Afrikaanse Melkbosskoenlapper

WINGSPAN: About 70 mm, sometimes considerably smaller.

SEXES: Similar, but males have four black spots on the hindwings, whereas females have only three.

DISTRIBUTION: Very common in the Cape Peninsula and throughout southern Africa. It flies from sea level up to high altitudes. Often visits flowers for their nectar.

FLIGHT PERIOD: The African Monarch is sometimes seen on warm days in midwinter, but in the Cape Peninsula it is most plentiful from about December until late May.

FOOD PLANTS AND EARLY STAGES: The larvae feed on Milkweeds from which they derive their poisonous properties, which they pass on to the pupae and adult butterflies. Milkweeds used in the Peninsula are, among others, various Wild Cottons *(Asclepia* spp.), Carrion flowers *(Stapelia variegata)* and Klimop *(Cynanchum* spp.).

The yellow-and-black-banded larva bears three pairs of movable filaments. The pupa is adorned with a half-girdle of gold above the abdomen, and six shiny golden spots on the thorax. Its ground colour varies considerably to blend in with its immediate surroundings. It is suspended head-down from a mat of silk.

NOTE: The unpalatable African Monarch is mimicked by, among others, the palatable female of the Common Diadem (69), which occasionally arrives in the Cape Peninsula from easterly districts. The male Diadem, although also palatable, does not mimic the African Monarch and bears no resemblance to the female Diadem, or Mimic, as it is also known. In the male African Monarch a fourth, larger black mark on the hindwing upperside represents a scent patch. It is made up of modified scales known as androconia. During courtship flights these scales release a chemical substance – an aphrodesiac – which, by the sweeping action of the two scent brushes situated at the tip of the abdomen, is scattered around the female. Thus the female is encouraged to mate.

Browns (Satyrines)

2 Table Mountain Beauty *Aëropetes tulbaghia* Bergprag

WINGSPAN: About 82 mm.

SEXES: Females usually larger than males and with an extra short yellow band on the forewing.

DISTRIBUTION: Table Mountain Beauty is widespread from the grassy mountain slopes of the Cape Peninsula throughout the Western Cape and up to the eastern mountainous areas of southern Africa into Zimbabwe.

FLIGHT PERIOD: Most plentiful from December until April, but individuals have been seen on the wing from late September, and some are still flying during May.

FOOD PLANTS AND EARLY STAGES: The female scatters her eggs among grasses such as Shade Ehrharta *(Ehrharta erecta)* and Common Thatch-grass *(Hyparrhenia hirta)*. The larvae feed on grass blades at night and rest at the grass roots during the day. They reach a length of up to 65 mm. The stout pupa is about 27 mm long. It is suspended head-down, and its colour matches its immediate surroundings.

NOTE: Table Mountain Beauty imbibes nectar mainly from red and pink flowers, and is regarded as the principal pollinator of at least 15 Fynbos flowers of those colours, including the striking Red Disa *(Disa uniflora)*. Red and pink flowers also lure this handsome butterfly into gardens situated at lower slopes.

1a African Monarch, ♂

1b African Monarch, freshly emerged ♀ underside

1c African Monarch, larva

1d African Monarch, pupa

2a Table Mountain Beauty, ♂

2b Table Mountain Beauty, ♀ underside

2c Table Mountain Beauty, larva

2d Table Mountain Beauty, pupa

3 Cape Autumn Widow   *Dira clytus clytus*   Kaapse Herfsweduwee

WINGSPAN: About 52 mm.

SEXES: Similar.

DISTRIBUTION: Common in the Cape Peninsula and in the entire Western Cape on grassy slopes, roadsides and waste grounds.

FLIGHT PERIOD: From March until May.

FOOD PLANTS AND EARLY STAGES: Females scatter eggs among grasses such as Shade Ehrharta *(Ehrharta erecta)* and Kikuyu *(Pennisetum clandestinum)*. Larvae feed during the night and rest among debris at the grass roots during the day, where, at a later stage, they also pupate. The species is single-brooded.

4 Mintha Widow   *Torynesis mintha mintha*   Minthaweduwee

WINGSPAN: About 46 mm.

SEXES: Similar.

DISTRIBUTION: Localised in the Cape Peninsula, it is found in such areas as Oudekraal, Red Hill near Simon's Town, the slopes of Signal Hill and the Silvermine Plateau. It is restricted to the Western Cape. The Mintha Widow often flies in the company of the Cape Autumn Widow, from which it is immediately distinguishable by the silver-coloured veins on the hindwing underside.

FLIGHT PERIOD: Late March until May.

FOOD PLANTS AND EARLY STAGES: Cape Wire Grass *(Merxmuellera stricta)* is the only known larval food plant. The larvae feed on the grass blades at night, and rest at the roots of the grass during the day. The pupae lie among debris at the roots of the host grass. The species is single-brooded.

3a Cape Autumn Widow, ♂

3b Cape Autumn Widow, ♀

3c Cape Autumn Widow, ♀ underside

3d Cape Autumn Widow, larva

3c Cape Autumn Widow, pupae

4a Mintha Widow, ♂

4b Mintha Widow, ♀

4c Mintha Widow, ♀ underside

4d Mintha Widow, larva

4e Mintha Widow, pupae

5 Cape Spring Widow *Tarsocera cassus cassus* Kaapse Lenteweduwee

WINGSPAN: About 44 mm.
SEXES: Similar.
DISTRIBUTION: Locally common in the Cape Peninsula and more or less restricted to the Western Cape, where it frequents grassy slopes of hills and mountains.
FLIGHT PERIOD: From late August until December.
FOOD PLANTS AND EARLY STAGES: The eggs are scattered among grasses such as Common Thatch-grass *(Hyparrhenia hirta)* and Rye Grass *(Lolium* spp.). The pale brown larvae feed at night and pupate among debris at the grass roots. This species is possibly double-brooded.

6 Sand-dune Widow *Tarsocera cassina* Duinweduwee

WINGSPAN: About 40 mm.
SEXES: Similar.
DISTRIBUTION: Restricted to the Western Cape. It occurs in a few places in the Cape Peninsula, such as the sandy coastal regions of the Cape Flats, including Strandfontein, Muizenberg and the sandy coastal and near-coastal low-lying areas from Milnerton Lighthouse northwards to well beyond Clanwilliam.
FLIGHT PERIOD: From early October until early December.
FOOD PLANTS AND EARLY STAGES: Rye Grass *(Lolium* spp.) is one of the grasses used by the larvae, but the early stages of the Sand-dune Widow are not well known. The Sand-dune Widow is probably double-brooded.

7 Trimen's Brown *Pseudonympha trimenii trimenii* Trimenbruintjie

WINGSPAN: About 36 mm.
SEXES: Similar.
DISTRIBUTION: Not common, but it can be found on the slopes of hills and mountains of the Cape Peninsula, in particular, Signal Hill, Lion's Head and across the Silvermine Plateau. It is confined to the Western Cape.
FLIGHT PERIOD: Only from September until November.
FOOD PLANTS AND EARLY STAGES: The larvae will feed on Cape Wire Grass *(Merxmuellera stricta)* and possibly other grass species. Both the larvae and pupae are grass-coloured. Trimen's Brown is a single-brooded species.

5a Cape Spring Widow, ♂

5b Cape Spring Widow, ♀

5c Cape Spring Widow, ♀ underside

5d Cape Spring Widow, pupae

6a Sand-dune Widow, ♂

6b Sand-dune Widow, ♀ underside

7a Trimen's Brown, ♂

7b Trimen's Brown, ♀ underside

8 Silver-bottom Brown *Pseudonympha magus* Towerbruintjie

WINGSPAN: About 35 mm. SEXES: Similar.

DISTRIBUTION: Common on marshy, grass-covered areas such as on the Cape Flats. In the Peninsula hills and mountains it is usually found on the wetter slopes. Its range of distribution extends into southern coastal or near-coastal areas of the Western and Eastern Cape.

FLIGHT PERIOD: October until May.

FOOD PLANTS AND EARLY STAGES: Eggs are laid on grasses such as Couch Grass *(Cynodon dactylon)* and Shade Ehrharta *(Ehrharta erecta)*. The colours of the larvae and pupae blend in well with that of the host plants. The Silver-bottom Brown is double-brooded.

9 Burchell's Brown *Pseudonympha hippia* Burchellbruintjie

WINGSPAN: About 39 mm. SEXES: Similar.

DISTRIBUTION: The summits of Table Mountain, Devil's Peak, the Twelve Apostles, Constantiaberg, and Muizenberg and Steenberg mountains. It also occurs on the summits of other mountains in the southern parts of the Western and Eastern Cape.

FLIGHT PERIOD: Late October until early March.

FOOD PLANTS AND EARLY STAGES: Certain reeds (*Thamnochortus glaber* and *Ischyrolepis capensis*), but larvae kept in captivity also feed on Shade Ehrharta (*Ehrharta erecta*). Both the larvae and the pupae have a cryptic coloration. The species is probably single-brooded.

10 Western Hillside Brown *Stygionympha vigilans* Rantbruintjie

WINGSPAN: About 43 mm. SEXES: Similar.

DISTRIBUTION: Common on grassy slopes of the Cape Peninsula, the entire Western and Eastern Cape and into KwaZulu-Natal.

FLIGHT PERIOD: September until April.

FOOD PLANTS AND EARLY STAGES: Shade Ehrharta *(Ehrharta erecta)* and certain reeds *(Ischyrolepis cincinnata)*. The final instar larva is brown with green stripes and tones in well with the colour of its host plants in summer. The pupa has not been described.

11 Rainforest Brown *Cassionympha cassius* Reënwoudbruintjie

WINGSPAN: About 32 mm. SEXES: Similar.

DISTRIBUTION: It dwells in humid coastal bush often near streams, wooded kloofs and in rainforests. It is not common in the Cape Peninsula, but can be found at Cecelia Forest beyond Kirstenbosch.

FLIGHT PERIOD: All year round, but very rarely seen during June and July in the Cape Peninsula.

FOOD PLANTS AND EARLY STAGES: Grasses including Tassel Grass *(Pentaschistis sp.)* and Rushes *(Juncus* spp.). Eggs are laid singly on blades of host plants. The generally reddish (sometimes green) larvae pupate suspended head-down. The pupa is greenish. The species is double-brooded.

12 Boland Brown *Melampias huebneri huebneri* Bolandbruintjie

WINGSPAN: About 36 mm. SEXES: Similar.

DISTRIBUTION: Common in the Cape Peninsula, and more or less restricted to the Western Cape.

FLIGHT PERIOD: July until November, with very few emergences also taking place during June under favourable conditions. Locally the Boland Brown is the earliest butterfly on the wing in numbers, and is regarded as the harbinger of spring.

FOOD PLANTS AND EARLY STAGES: The larvae feed on grasses such as Wild Oats *(Avena sativa)* and Shade Ehrharta *(Ehrharta erecta)*. They estivate during the dry summer months. Pupation takes place during June and July. The species is single-brooded.

8a Silver-bottom Brown, ♂

8b Silver-bottom Brown,
♂ underside

9a Burchell's Brown, ♂

9b Burchell's Brown, ♀ underside

10a Western Hillside Brown, ♂

10b Western Hillside Brown,
♂ underside

11a Rainforest Brown, ♂

11b Rainforest Brown,
♀ underside

12a Boland Brown, ♂

12b Boland Brown, ♀ underside

Acraeas (Acraeines)

13 Garden Acraea *Acraea horta* Tuinrooitjie

WINGSPAN: About 50 mm.

SEXES: Male a brighter red than female.

DISTRIBUTION: The Garden Acraea is very common in the Cape Peninsula and throughout most of South Africa, but it is absent from the dry Bushveld. It is frequently encountered in gardens and is easily recognised by its reddish colours and leisurely flight.

FLIGHT PERIOD: All year round, but scarce during the winter months.

FOOD PLANTS AND EARLY STAGES: The larvae feed on Wild Peach *(Kiggelaria africana)* and certain Passion Flowers *(Passiflora* sp.), but not the edible Granadilla *(Passiflora edulis)*. The eggs are laid in batches of up to 150 eggs on leaves of the food plant. The yellow-and-black pupae are often seen in exposed positions on walls and fences situated near the food plants.

NOTE: Although shunned by vertebrate predators, the larvae and pupae of the Garden Acraea are usually heavily parasitised, mostly by parasitic wasps, but a Bristle Fly also attacks the mature larvae and pupae. Unlike some of its congeners, the unpalatable Garden Acraea is not mimicked by other butterflies. Klaas's Cuckoo *(Chrysococcyx klaas)* is said to eat the distasteful larvae.

Nymphs (Nymphalines)

14 Painted Lady *Vanessa cardui* Sondagsrokkie

WINGSPAN: About 50 mm.

SEXES: Similar.

DISTRIBUTION: Very common in the Cape Peninsula and throughout southern Africa. It also occurs in Australia, America and Europe. It is often seen in gardens.

FLIGHT PERIOD: All year round, even on sunny days in winter. In spring and summer males are often seen flying back and forth over their territories, chasing each other until sunset.

FOOD PLANTS AND EARLY STAGES: A variety of plants belonging to unrelated families such as *Arctotis* spp., Bread-and-Butter Plant *(Malva parviflora)*, *Calendula* spp., Cape Weed *(Arctotheca calendula)*, Daisies *(Dimorphotheca* spp.), *Gazania* species, Nettles *(Urtica* sp.) and Thistles *(Carduus* spp.). The larvae spin a protective web over themselves on the leaves on which they are feeding. The handsome pupa has a metallic sheen and is usually found on or near the larval food plant.

NOTE: The Painted Lady possesses well-developed, strong wing muscles, which enable it to migrate over long distances – even across the seas. However, in South and southern Africa their migratory movements are much more restricted.

13a Garden Acraea, ♂

13b Garden Acraea, ♀ ovipositing

13c Garden Acraea, larva

13d Garden Acraea, pupa

14a Painted Lady, ♂

14b Painted Lady, ♀ newly emerged

14c Painted Lady, larva

14d Painted Lady, pupa

Blues and Coppers (Lycaenids)

15 Boland Skolly *Thestor protumnus protumnus* Bolandskollie

WINGSPAN: About 30 mm. SEXES: Females usually larger than males.
DISTRIBUTION: In the Cape Peninsula this rather rare species is restricted to Red Hill above Simon's Town and the odd spot on Silvermine Plateau.
FLIGHT PERIOD: September until December.
FOOD SOURCE AND EARLY STAGES: The larvae of this Yellow Skolly are associated with the Pugnacious Ant *(Anplolepis custodiens)*, but their source of food is not known. The early instar larvae of certain other Yellow Skollies feed on tiny plant-sucking bugs and scale insects, but the diet of their later instar larvae has not been determined with certainty. It can be assumed that the early instar larvae of the Boland Skolly live on a similar diet. The species is single-brooded.

16 Peninsula Skolly *Thestor yildizae* Skiereilandskollie

WINGSPAN: About 30 mm. SEXES: Females usually larger than males.
DISTRIBUTION: This Dark Skolly is only found in the Cape Peninsula, where it is common on the Table Mountain range, the Muizenberg mountains and the Silvermine Plateau.
FLIGHT PERIOD: Late November until February.
FOOD SOURCE AND EARLY STAGES: Reared in captivity, freshly emerged larvae were picked up by Pugnacious Ants *(Anplolepis custodiens)*, their host ants, and placed inside their nests, where they soon died. The food source of these tiny larvae has not yet been determined, but the later instar larvae stay permanently in their host ant's nests, where they solicit food by swaying their tiny heads in front of approaching ants. The ants then feed the larvae by regurgitating food into the mouths of the begging larvae (trophallaxis), a method of feeding commonly used between ants of the same colony, and between worker ants and queens and ant larvae.

After several moults the larvae pupate, also inside the host ants' nests. Freshly emerged adults delay wing expansion until they have found the exit from the nest used by the ants. The ants often visit their guest larvae, which do not possess a honey gland, but produce an ant-attracting substance from tiny glands found in their skin. The ants press their mouth parts on these glands, as well as those found on the pupae, and take in their secretion. The exact nature of the secretion of these glands is not known, but it obviously confuses the ants to such an extent that they treat the guest larvae and pupae as their own brood. In their natural environment, colonies of these ants have been found to individually nurture several of these Skolly larvae. This species is single-brooded, and in its immature stages spends about 10 months underground in the host ants' nests.

17 Protea Scarlet *Capys alphaeus* Suikerbossieskoenlapper

WINGSPAN: Males about 34 mm, females up to 45 mm.
SEXES: Similar, but females usually larger than males.
DISTRIBUTION: The Cape Peninsula, the entire Western Cape and far beyond, in Fynbos that includes suitable Proteas.
FOOD PLANTS AND EARLY STAGES: Eggs are laid on Protea buds, usually one per bud. The larvae enters the bud and feeds on the developing reproductive parts, thus destroying the Protea flower. The larvae, in spite of possessing a small honey gland in the later instars, have not been recorded being attended by ants. Pupation takes place inside the bud, and emergence of the adult occurs through a hole made large enough by the larva prior to pupation. Common Proteas used include the King Protea *(Protea cynaroides)* and Sugarbush *(Protea repens)* (see Fig. 1 p. 6).
NOTE: The pretty Protea Scarlet is much less common in the Cape Peninsula than it used to be due to a decrease in the number of Protea bushes.

15a Boland Skolly, ♂, ♀

15b Boland Skolly, ♀ underside

16a Peninsula Skolly, ♂, ♀

16b Peninsula Skolly, underside

16c Peninsula Skolly,
mature larva fed by
its host ant

16d Peninsula Skolly, pupae in host ants' nest

17a Protea Scarlet, ♀, ♂

17b Protea Scarlet, ♂ underside

18 Silver Arrowhead *Phasis thero thero* Silwerpylkoppie

WINGSPAN: Males about 37 mm.

SEXES: Similar, but females usually larger than males.

DISTRIBUTION: In the Cape Peninsula the Silver Arrowhead may be found at Strandfontein and in suitable localities around the coast. It flies from Namaqualand to at least as far as Knynsa, but is absent from the Table Mountain range itself.

FLIGHT PERIOD: August until April.

FOOD PLANTS AND EARLY STAGES: The larvae feed on leaves of Honeybush *(Melianthus major)*, Kuni-bush *(Rhus undulata)* and other *Rhus* species. The larvae are associated with Cocktail Ants *(Crematogaster* spp.). During the day the larvae shelter in hollow stems of Honeybushes and in crevices in the stems of *Rhus* bushes, where they are continuously attended by the ants. During the night they leave their shelters in the company of ants to feed on the leaves of the food plants. They also pupate in these shelters. Occasionally larvae and pupae are found in these shelters without ants being anywhere near them, at least during the day time.

19 Scarce Mountain Copper *Trimenia malagrida malagrida* Seldsame Bergkopervlerkie

WINGSPAN: About 27 mm.

SEXES: Females larger than males.

DISTRIBUTION: This protected butterfly, also known as Lion's Head Copper, now appears to be restricted to one or two small areas on the Table Mountain range. It is feared that the butterfly may have disappeared from its last well-known haunts.

FLIGHT PERIOD: February until April.

FOOD SOURCE AND EARLY STAGES: Many attempts have been made to unravel the ant-associated life history of this butterfly. Larvae bred from eggs have refused to feed on likely food plants. No later instars nor pupae have been found. Late instar larvae and pupae of a subspecies of this rare butterfly occurring outside the Peninsula have been found in nests of the Pugnacious Ant *(Anoplolepis custodiens)*, but the larval diet has not been determined with certainty .

NOTE: Colonies of the now endangered butterfly were once known from various localities on the Table Mountain range, but it is believed that repeated mountain fires, coinciding with the butterfly's short late-summer flight period, have caused the near or even total extinction of this pretty Copper.

18a Silver Arrowhead, ♂

18b Silver Arrowhead, ♀

18c Silver Arrowhead, ♀ ovipositing on Honeybush

18d Silver Arrowhead, larva with attending Cocktail Ant

18e Silver Arrowhead, pupa

19a Scarce Mountain Copper, ♂, ♀

19b Scarce Mountain Copper, ♂ in resting position

19c Scarce Mountain Copper, ♂ underside

20 Red Copper *Aloeides thyra thyra* Berkopervlerkie

WINGSPAN: About 26 mm.

SEXES: Females often larger than males.

DISTRIBUTION: Common in the Cape Peninsula and more or less restricted to the Western Cape.

FLIGHT PERIOD: Late August until May.

FOOD PLANTS AND EARLY STAGES: The larvae feed on Prickly Pea-bushes *(Aspalathus* spp.). They are closely associated with the Small Black Sugar Ant *(Lepisiota capensis).* The larvae, at least the later instars, shelter in their nests during the day and, accompanied by the ants, leave their nests after sunset to feed on nearby food plants. Again accompanied by the ants, they return to the safety of their nests before dawn. During the driest summer months the larvae estivate. They pupate in the host ants' nest during July or August to produce adults about three weeks later in August or September. This spring brood produces a second brood in summer. The pupae are constantly attended by the ants.

20a Red Copper, ♂, ♀

20b Red Copper, ♂ feeding

20c Red Copper, mating pair

20d Red Copper, larvae in nest of Small Black Sugar Ant

20e Red Copper, larva feeding at night, attended by host ants

20f Red Copper, pupa with host ant

21 Aranda Copper *Aloeides aranda* Arandakopervlerkie

WINGSPAN: About 27 mm.
SEXES: Females usually larger than males.
DISTRIBUTION: In the Cape Peninsula the Aranda Copper occurs on the Twelve Apostles, Red Hill above Simon's Town, the Vlakkenberg above Constantia Nek, and the hills above Scarborough. It occurs in most if not all the provinces of South Africa.
FLIGHT PERIOD: From late September until April, with a few emergences during January and February.
FOOD PLANTS AND EARLY STAGES: The larvae feed on *Aspalathus* species, including Prickly Pea-bushes *(Aspalathus* spp.). They have been observed to be visited by the small workers of the Brown House Ant *(Pheidole capensis)*, which imbibe the secretion of their honey gland, both in their natural environment and in captivity. The larvae shelter in the sand and debris at the base of the stem of the food plant from where they, accompanied by the ants, crawl up the stem at night to feed on the leaves.

22 Almeida Copper *Aloeides almeida* Grasveldkopervlerkie

WINGSPAN: About 25 mm.
SEXES: Females usually larger than males.
DISTRIBUTION: Localised but not uncommon on the Peninsula mountains, including the Table Mountain range and Silvermine Plateau. It is restricted to the Western Cape. It occurs at both high and low altitudes.
FLIGHT PERIOD: Late September until April.
FOOD PLANTS AND EARLY STAGES: The larval food plant has not been determined and neither the larva nor the pupa have been found or reared. The larvae would most likely be associated with ants and feed on *Aspalathus* species.

23 Dull Copper *Aloeides pierus* Kaapse kopervlerkie

WINGSPAN: About 28 mm.
SEXES: Females usually larger than males.
DISTRIBUTION: Common in the Peninsula, the entire Western Cape and beyond in montane Fynbos.
FLIGHT PERIOD: Late September until April.
FOOD PLANTS AND EARLY STAGES: The larvae feed on *Aspalathus* species including Prickly Pea-bushes. They have been found in nests of the Small Black Sugar Ant *(Lepisiota capensis)*. Placed in an artificial ants' nest, it was noticed that the larvae were constantly attended by the ants which, as in the Red Copper, accompany them to and from their food plants at night. The larvae pupate in or near their host ants' nests, where the pupae are constantly visited by the ants. The Dull Copper is double-brooded, with a spring and an autumn brood. Few emergences occur during midsummer.

21a Aranda Copper, ♂, ♀   21b Aranda Copper, ♀ underside   21c Aranda Copper, larva, late instar

22a Almeida Copper, ♂, ♀   22b Almeida Copper, ♀ underside

23a Dull Copper, ♂, ♀   23b Dull Copper, ♀ underside

23c Dull Copper, ♀ resting on the ground   23d Dull Copper, larva, late instar

BLUES AND COPPERS (Lycaenids)   29

24 Red Hill Copper *Aloeides egerides* Rooiheuwelkopervlerkie

WINGSPAN: About 29 mm.

SEXES: Females usually larger than males.

DISTRIBUTION: In the Cape Peninsula this protected species occurs sparingly on Red Hill above Simon's Town and on the hills above Scarborough. Restricted to the Western Cape, it occurs in Fynbos environments, and in places such as Mamre, Picketberg, Struisbaai and Hermanus.

FLIGHT PERIOD: From October (spring brood) until April (autumn brood). The butterfly is rarely encountered during January and February.

FOOD PLANTS AND EARLY STAGES: Not known, but they would be similar to those of related Coppers.

25 Burnished Copper *Chrysoritis chrysaor* Besemboskopervlerkie

WINGSPAN: About 25 mm.

SEXES: Females usually larger than males.

DISTRIBUTION: Although widespread throughout South Africa, in the Cape Peninsula the Burnished Copper only occurs at higher altitudes, such as the Silvermine Plateau and Red Hill. It usually flies singly or in pairs. It appears to be absent from the Table Mountain range itself.

FLIGHT PERIOD: In the Cape Peninsula, it is most often encountered during the warmer spring and summer months.

FOOD PLANTS AND EARLY STAGES: The larvae feed on Pig's Ears *(Cotyledon orbiculata)*, certain *Rhus* species, and Tortoise Bushes *(Zygophyllum* spp.). They are attended by ants, but no details are known about their association.

24a Red Hill Copper, ♂, ♀

24b Red Hill Copper, ♂ and ♀ underside

25a Burnished Copper, ♂, ♀

25b Burnished Copper, ♂ underside

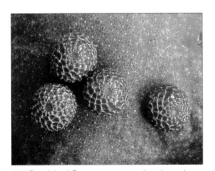

25c Burnished Copper, eggs, much enlarged

25d Burnished Copper, larva, final instar

26 Common Opal *Chrysoritis thysbe thysbe* Pragopaal

WINGSPAN: Males about 25 mm.

SEXES: Females often larger than males.

DISTRIBUTION: In the Cape Peninsula the Common Opal occurs on Red Hill and Silvermine Plateau, in the Cape of Good Hope Nature Reserve, at Hout Bay and at Strandfontein. Outside the Peninsula it occurs from Lambert's Bay to Milnerton Lighthouse in the west, to at least as far as Mossel Bay in the east. It is more or less restricted to the Western Cape.

FLIGHT PERIOD: From August right through to April or May.

FOOD PLANTS AND EARLY STAGES: The larvae feed on Bush-tick Berry *(Chrysanthemoides incana, Thesium* species, Tortoise Bushes *(Zygophyllum sessifolium, Z. flexuosum* and *Z. morgsana)*, and others. They are always associated with Cocktail Ants *(Crematogaster* spp.), which build shelters for them at the base of the food plants. There the ants attend to them during the day and accompany them to where they feed at night. Pupation also occurs in these shelters. The Common Opal is multi-brooded.

NOTE: The beautiful Common Opal occurs in two forms. In form *thysbe*, dark and light markings are clearly evident on the hindwing underside. In form *osbecki* this side is not clearly marked and of an almost uniform brownish colour. The uppersides of the two forms are identical. Intermediate forms also occur.

27 Sand-dune Opal *Chrysoritis pyroeis pyroeis* Duinkopervlerkie

WINGSPAN: Up to 30 mm, females up to 36 mm.

SEXES: Females sometimes considerably larger than males.

DISTRIBUTION: In the Cape Peninsula the Sand-dune Opal occurs on Red Hill, on the slopes above St James and at Strandfontein. It occurs in many places both at sea level and at high altitude from Hondeklipbaai in Namaqualand to Stilbaai on the south coast.

FLIGHT PERIOD: September to April, but most plentiful during September and October, and again from February until April.

FOOD PLANTS AND EARLY STAGES: The larvae feed on Tortoise Bushes *(Zygophyllum flexuosum)* and *Thesium* species. They are associated with a Droptail Ant *(Myrmecaria* sp.), which builds shelters for them at the base of their food plants. Accompanied by the ants, they vacate the shelters at night to feed and return to them before dawn. The species is double-brooded.

26a Common Opal ♂, ♀

26b Common Opal, ♂ underside, form *thysbe*

26c Common Opal, ♂ underside, form *osbecki*

26d Common Opal, larva with Cocktail Ant

27a Sand-dune Opal ♂, ♀

27b Sand-dune Opal, ♀ underside

27c Sand-dune Opal, larva

27d Sand-dune Opal, larva with Droptail Ant imbibing the secretion of its honey gland

28 Dark Opal *Chrysoritis nigricans nigricans* Bloujuweelopaal

WINGSPAN: About 26 mm.

SEXES: Females do not resemble males on the upperside of the wings.

DISTRIBUTION: In the Cape Peninsula this protected and exquisite butterfly was once known from several spots on Table Mountain, where it still exists on the back table. It also occurred, and may still occur, on the Silvermine Plateau, Red Hill, and possibly other mountains of the Peninsula towards Cape Point. Its distribution is restricted to the Western Cape, where it still flies in low-lying areas as well as at high altitudes, from Mamre on the West Coast, to Franschhoek, Hermanus, Bredasdorp and Calitzdorp in the east.

FLIGHT PERIOD: Most likely to be seen during September and October, and again from February until April.

FOOD PLANTS AND EARLY STAGES: The larvae feed on Bitou (*Osteospermum polygaloides*), *Thesium* species and Tortoise Bushes (*Zygophyllum* spp.). Cocktail Ants (*Crematogaster* spp.) build papery shelters around the larvae in which they, attended by the ants, rest in the day. Accompanied by the ants, they leave the shelters at night to feed on the food plants. The Dark Opal is double-brooded.

29 Feltham's Opal *Chrysoritis felthami felthami* Felthamkopervlerkie

WINGSPAN: Males up to 27 mm, females up to 32 mm.

SEXES: Females usually larger than males.

DISTRIBUTION: Close to Cape Town it occurs from Milnerton northwards to Namaqualand. It has been recorded from the Cape Flats and locally at Strandfontein. It has not been recorded from any of the Peninsula mountains.

FLIGHT PERIOD: Late September until April with few specimens on the wing from December until mid-February.

FOOD PLANTS AND EARLY STAGES: The larvae feed on Tortoise Bushes (*Zygophyllum sessifolium* and *Z. flexuosum*). They build shelters at the base of the food plant using silk to stick together sand and bits of debris. Sometimes a number of larvae hide in the same shelter during the day, where they are attended by Cocktail Ants (*Crematogaster* spp.). They also pupate in these shelters. The species is double-brooded.

30 Water Opal *Chrysoritis palmus palmus* Wateropaal

WINGSPAN: About 26 mm.

SEXES: Females usually larger than males

DISTRIBUTION: In the Cape Peninsula the Water Opal occurs in Orange Kloof Nature Reserve, on Red Hill above Simon's Town, and the mountains above St James, and is comparatively common above Scarborough. It is restricted to the Western Cape. It is usually found near streams and in marshy habitats.

FLIGHT PERIOD: September until April.

FOOD PLANTS AND EARLY STAGES: The larvae feed on Kolkol (*Berzelia* spp.), Bitou (*Osteospermum polygaloides*), Bush-tick Berry (*Chrysanthemoides monilifera*), and other plants. They are attended by Cocktail Ants (*Crematogaster* spp.), which build papery shelters for them on the food plant (see Fig. 2 p. 7). The species is double-brooded.

28a Dark Opal ♂, ♀

28b Dark Opal, ♂ underside

28c Dark Opal, egg, much enlarged

28d Dark Opal, larva

29a Feltham's Opal ♂, ♀

29b Feltham's Opal, ♀ underside

29c Feltham's Opal, larva, late instar

30a Water Opal ♂, ♀

30b Water Opal, ♀ underside

30c Water Opal, in resting position

30d Water Opal, larva, final instar

31 Jitterbug Daisy Copper *Chrysoritis zeuxo* Suidkuskopervlerkie

WINGSPAN: About 26 mm.

SEXES: Similar.

DISTRIBUTION: More or less confined to the Western Cape as far as Knysna. Having been more plentiful in the past in the Cape Peninsula, this Copper now only occurs in a few places in kloofs of the Table Mountain range, on Red Hill above Simon's Town, at Strandfontein, and on the Cape Flats.

FLIGHT PERIOD: Late September until January.

FOOD PLANTS AND EARLY STAGES: The larvae feed on Bush-tick Berry *(Chrysanthemoides monilifera)*, and are associated with Cocktail Ants *(Crematogaster* spp.). The species is single-brooded and is always found on or near its larval food plant.

32 Donkey Daisy Copper *Chrysoritis zonarius* Donkiekopervlerkie

WINGSPAN: About 24 mm.

SEXES: Similar.

DISTRIBUTION: The Donkey Daisy Copper is confined to the Western Cape Province. This butterfly has become rare in the Cape Peninsula, occurring only in one threatened habitat near the coast at Camp's Bay. It is, however, found abundantly in coastal bush northwards from Milnerton.

FLIGHT PERIOD: September until November.

FOOD PLANTS AND EARLY STAGES: The larvae feed on Bush-tick Berry *(Chrysanthemoides incana)*. Cocktail Ants *(Crematogaster* spp.) are always present where the larvae are feeding.

33 Vivid Blue *Tarucus thespis* Fynbosspikkelbloutjie

WINGSPAN: About 23 mm.

SEXES: Differ in colour and markings on the upperside.

DISTRIBUTION: The Vivid or Azure Blue is common on all mountains of the Cape Peninsula. It is most plentiful in and near coastal areas, but it also flies in inland habitats of the Western and Eastern Cape provinces.

FLIGHT PERIOD: All year round. Adults emerge on sunny days, even in midwinter.

FOOD PLANTS AND EARLY STAGES: The green larvae feed on common Fynbos plants such as Hard-leaf Bushes *(Phylica imberbis)* and *Saxifraga* species. They are well equiped for ant association. One record exists of the Argentine Ant *(Linepithema humile)* visiting them. Pupation usually occurs near the base of the food plant.

31a Jitterbug Daisy Copper ♂, ♀

31b Jitterbug Daisy Copper, ♀ underside

31c Jitterbug Daisy Copper, egg, much enlarged

31d Jitterbug Daisy Copper, larva, first instar

32a Donkey Daisy Copper ♂, ♀

32b Donkey Daisy Copper, ♀ underside

32c Donkey Daisy Copper, larva, final instar

33a Vivid Blue ♂, ♀

33b Vivid Blue, ♂ underside

33c Vivid Blue, larva on Hard-leaf Bush

34 Cupreous Blue *Eichochrysops messapus messapus* Koperbloutjie

WINGSPAN: About 19 mm.
SEXES: Females darker in colour than males.
DISTRIBUTION: Common on hills and mountains of the Cape Peninsula and throughout the Western and Eastern Cape.
FLIGHT PERIOD: September to May with a few emergences of adults also taking place on sunny days in midwinter.
FOOD PLANTS AND EARLY STAGES: Females oviposit on flower buds of *Thesium* species. The larvae feed on the buds and young seed pods. They possess a honey gland and other structures, which suggest that they are associated with ants. The pupa is attached to a support on or near the food plant.

35 Lucerne Blue *Lampides boeticus* Lusernbloutjie

WINGSPAN: 28 to 32 mm, but considerably smaller individuals are often found, especially during the driest summer months.
SEXES: Females differ in upperside markings.
DISTRIBUTION: Widely distributed throughout the Cape Peninsula and, in fact, the whole of Africa, as well as the warmer parts of Europe and other parts of the world. It is often encountered in urban gardens.
FLIGHT PERIOD: Being multi-brooded, the Lucerne Blue is found on the wing almost throughout the year, but in the Peninsula it becomes scarce during the colder winter months.
FOOD PLANTS AND EARLY STAGES: The larvae feed on many leguminous plants including Lucerne *(Medicago sativa)*, Cancer Bush *(Sutherlandia frutescens)*, Keurboom *(Virgilia oroboides)*, cultivated peas and beans, and many others. The eggs are laid on flowers and young seed pods. The larvae feed on these parts and on the growing seeds inside the pods. They are well adapted for ant association, and have often been observed in attendence of the Small Black Sugar Ant *(Lepisiota capensis)* inside seed pods. The larvae pupate in sheltered positions on or near the food plants. When a number of these larvae are placed together, even with a fresh supply of food plant in a small container, they tend to turn cannibalistic, and devour dormant moulting or pupating larvae of their own kind.

36 Common Blue *Leptotis pirithous* Gewone Bloutjie

WINGSPAN: About 25 mm.
SEXES: Females differ from males in markings on the uppersides of wings.
DISTRIBUTION: Common in the Cape Peninsula and throughout southern Africa.
FLIGHT PERIOD: Throughout the year, becoming rare during the winter months.
FOOD PLANTS AND EARLY STAGES: The larvae feed on buds and flowers of Plumbago *(Plumbago auriculata)*, Cape Honeysuckle *(Tecomaria capensis)*, Keurboom *(Virgilia oroboides)*, Lucerne *(Medicago sativa)* and several other plants. They possess a honey gland, and ants have been recorded visiting them. However, on Plumbago *(Plumbago auriculata)* small ants get stuck in the sticky substance secreted by the calyces of the flower. This substance does not entrap the larvae. The pupa is supported by a girdle and tiny hooks (cremastral hooks) against a mat of silk spun by the larva prior to pupation. The species is multi-brooded.

34a Cupreous Blue ♂, ♀

34b Cupreous Blue,
♂ underside

35a Lucerne Blue ♂, ♀

35b Lucerne Blue, ♂ underside

35c Lucerne Blue, larva in a
pod of Cancer Bush

36a Common Blue ♂, ♀

36b Common Blue, ♂ underside

36c Common Blue, larva

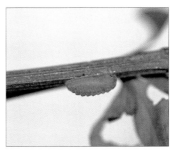

36d Common Blue, larva pupating

37 Short-toothed Blue *Leptotis brevidentatus* Kortgetandebloutjie

This species very closely resembles the Common Blue in outward appearance, uses the same food plants and, in some places, the look-alikes fly together. The two species can be separated with certainty by comparing the internal genital apparatus of the males. The Short-toothed Blue has been recorded at several places in the Cape Peninsula, including Cape Town. It is best known from the eastern parts of South Africa and far beyond.

38 Bush Blue *Cacyreus lingeus* Bosbloutjie

WINGSPAN: About 25 mm, but often smaller during the dry summer months.
SEXES: Markings on the uppersides of the wings distinguish females from males.
DISTRIBUTION: Common in the Cape Peninsula and throughout southern Africa. It frequents places where its larval food plants grow along streams, in the Bushveld and on dry mountain slopes.
FLIGHT PERIOD: Throughout the year, but very scarce during winter.
FOOD PLANTS AND EARLY STAGES: The larvae feed on buds and flowers of fragrant plants including the Spur-flower *(Plectranthus* spp.), Blue Sage *(Salvia africana-caerulea)* and Golden Sage *(S. africana-lutea)*, as well as the common garden herbs, Sage *(Salvia* spp.), Lavender *(Lavendula* spp.) and Mint *(Mentha* spp.). The larvae possess a honey gland, but ants have not been recorded visiting them. The small hairy pupa matches its immediate surroundings in colour and is supported by a girdle and tiny cremastral hooks at its posterior end. The species is multi-brooded.

39 Common Geranium Bronze *Cacyreus marshalli* Gewone Malvabrons

WINGSPAN: About 20 mm, but late summer specimens can be much smaller and in early spring, strikingly large individuals are found, especially among the females.
SEXES: Similar.
DISTRIBUTION: Very common in the Cape Peninsula and widespread in southern Africa. It occurs both at sea level and at high altitudes. It is often found on *Geranium* species and *Pelargonium* species in gardens. It has spread from South Africa to Spain, where it has become a serious pest, its larvae devouring all *Geranium* flowers.
FLIGHT PERIOD: All year round, but very scarce during winter.
FOOD PLANTS AND EARLY STAGES: The larvae feed on buds and flowers of *Geranium* and *Pelargonium* species. They are not associated with ants. The small, hairy pupae vary in colour to match their surroundings. They are supported by a girdle and cremastral hooks. The Common Geranium Bronze is double-brooded.

40 Dickson's Geranium Bronze *Cacyreus dicksoni* Dicksonmalvabrons

This species is closely related to the Common Geranium Bronze, and it is hard to distinguish between the two with the naked eye. It has been recorded from the Cape Peninsula, but it is most widely distributed in the arid regions of the Western Cape Province and Namaqualand. Although only small differences can be observed on both the upperside and underside, it can be distinguished with certainty from its double by comparing the internal genitalia of the males. The habits, food plants and early stages of the two species are very similar.

37 Short-toothed Blue ♂, ♀
underside

38a Bush Blue ♂, ♀

38b Bush Blue, ♂ underside

39a Common Geranium Bronze ♂, ♀

39b Common Geranium Bronze,
♀ underside

39c Common Geranium Bronze, larva

39d Common Geranium Bronze, pupa

40a Dickson's Geranium Bronze ♂, ♀

40b Dickson's Geranium Bronze,
♀ underside

41 Water Bronze   *Cacyreus palemon palemon*   Waterbrons

WINGSPAN: About 20 mm.
SEXES: Similar.
DISTRIBUTION: Common in the Cape Peninsula and throughout South Africa. It occurs both at sea level and on higher mountain slopes. It frequents damp places, such as along streams.
FLIGHT PERIOD: Most common from August until May.
FOOD PLANTS AND EARLY STAGES: The larvae feed on buds and flowers of *Pelargonium* species and *Geranium* species. They are not associated with ants. The small, hairy pupa is supported by a girdle and cremastral hooks.

42 Sooty Blue   *Zizeeria knysna*   Dubbletjiebloutjie

WINGSPAN: About 21 mm.
SEXES: Females are darker than males.
DISTRIBUTION: This little butterfly is widely distributed throughout South and southern Africa. It also occurs in Europe. In the Cape Peninsula it is particularly common, both at high and low altitudes. It occurs in all gardens.
FLIGHT PERIOD: All year round. In its favourite haunts, it is often seen on the wing on sunny days in midwinter.
FOOD PLANTS AND EARLY STAGES: The larvae feed on Devil's Thorn *(Tribulus terrestris)*, Sorrel *(Oxalis* spp.), Lucerne *(Medicago sativa)*, and other common plants. Certain ants have been recorded visiting the larvae. Pupation occurs among debris under the food plant.

43 Western Sorrel Copper   *Lycaena orus*   Kleinkopervlerkie

WINGSPAN: About 22 mm. In late summer smaller specimens are not uncommon.
SEXES: Females usually larger than males.
DISTRIBUTION: The number of colonies known from the Cape Peninsula, particularly from the Table Mountain range, is dwindling rapidly, but strong colonies exist on the nearby Tygerberg Hills. Repeated fires that destroy stands of its larval food plants are responsible for the disappearance of this beautiful Copper from several of its former habitats. The species also occurs on various Western and Eastern Cape mountains as far as Port Elizabeth.
FLIGHT PERIOD: All year round, but very scarce during winter.
FOOD PLANTS AND EARLY STAGES: The larvae feed on Knotweed *(Polygonum* spp.) and possibly Dock *(Rumex lanceolatus)*. They are not associated with ants. Pupation occurs against a stem of the food plant.

44 Cape Black-eye   *Leptomyrina lara*   Kaapse Swartogie

WINGSPAN: About 24 mm.
SEXES: Females usually larger than males.
DISTRIBUTION: Common in the Cape Peninsula and throughout the Western Cape and far beyond.
FLIGHT PERIOD: Throughout the year, but less common during winter.
FOOD PLANTS AND EARLY STAGES: The eggs are laid on leaves of Pig's Ears *(Cotyledon orbiculata)* and related succulent perennials. The larvae burrow into the fleshy leaves and feed, moult and pupate inside them. The larvae have a honey gland, but no ants have been seen to attend them. The species is multi-brooded.

41a Water Bronze ♂, ♀

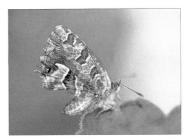

41b Water Bronze, ♀ underside

42a Sooty Blue ♂, ♀

42b Sooty Blue, ♀ underside

43a Western Sorrel Copper ♂, ♀

43b Western Sorrel Copper, ♀ underside

44a Cape Black-eye ♂, ♀

44b Cape Black-eye, ♀ underside

45 Common Hairtail *Anthene definita definita* Donkerkortstertjie

WINGSPAN: About 25 mm.

SEXES: The males differ from the females both in colour and in the markings on the upperside of the wings.

DISTRIBUTION: Common in the Cape Peninsula and throughout the coastal districts of South Africa.

FLIGHT PERIOD: All year round, but most plentiful from September until April or May.

FOOD PLANTS AND EARLY STAGES: The larvae feed on buds and flowers of many plants such as Jacket-plum *(Pappea capensis)*, Sweet Thorn *(Acacia karroo)*, Sweet Chestnut *(Castanea sativa)*, Port Jackson Willow *(Acacia saligna)*, Black Wattle *(Acacia mearnsii)*, Boerboon *(Schotia* spp.), etc. The larva has a saw-toothed appearance dorsally, and the dorsum of the pupa is adorned with a white diamond-shaped mark. The large Spotted Sugar Ant *(Camponotus maculatus)*, the Small Black Sugar Ant *(Lepisiota capensis)* and the Brown House Ant *(Pheidole capensis)* have been observed imbibing the sweet secretion of the larva's honey gland. The Argentine Ant *(Linepithema humile)* has also been recorded visiting a larva.

46 Monkey Blue *Lepidochrysops methymna methymna* Bobbejaanbloutjie

WINGSPAN: About 38 mm.

SEXES: Similar.

DISTRIBUTION: This Dark Blue inhabits the hills and mountains of the Western Cape. It is common in the Cape Peninsula, including the Table Mountain range.

FLIGHT PERIOD: Late September until January, but most likely to be seen from October until December.

FOOD SOURCE AND EARLY STAGES: In the Cape Peninsula the female oviposits on flower buds of Cape Blue Haze *(Selago spuria)* and Tooth-leaf Selago *(Selago serrata)*. The early instar larvae feed on the flowers of these plants and, during the night, are visited by the large Spotted Sugar Ant *(Camponotus maculatus)*. These ants imbibe the sweet secretion of the honey gland on the larvae. After their second moult (in their third instar), when visited by these ants the larvae loosen their grip on the flowers and roll themselves up almost into a ball. Thus they allow the ants to carry them off to their nests, where they deposit them among the brood. In the hosts' nest, the larvae soon moult again, lose their honey gland and become carnivorous. The ants allow the larvae to devour their own brood in return for a sweet secretion from the glands in their skin. In spring, after having spent about 10 months in the host ants' nest, the larvae pupate. The pupae are also visited by the ants, which derive some secretion from glands in the pupal skin or from their hair-like hollow spines. After three weeks the adults emerge and swiftly escape from the ants' nest before inflating their wings to start their adult life.

Fig. 6. A Sugar Ant carrying a third instar larva of a Monkey Blue to its nest.

45a Common Hairtail ♂, ♀

45b Common Hairtail, ♀ underside

45c Common Hairtail, larva on Black Wattle

45d Common Hairtail, pupa

46a Monkey Blue ♂, ♀

46b Monkey Blue, ♂ underside

46c Monkey Blue, larva feeding on pupa of Spotted Sugar Ant

47 Trimen's Blue *Lepidochrysops trimeni* Trimenbloutjie

WINGSPAN: About 37 mm.

SEXES: The females are distinguishable from the males by the dark markings on the uppersides of the wings.

DISTRIBUTION: This truly blue species is common on the Table Mountain range and other mountains of the Cape Peninsula, including Red Hill. Further afield it occurs on the Franschhoek and Du Toit's Kloof mountains, as well as on other mountains of the Western Cape.

FLIGHT PERIOD: September until January, but most likely to be seen from October until December.

FOOD PLANTS AND EARLY STAGES: In the Cape Peninsula the food plants of the early instar larvae are the same as those of the Monkey Blue (46). The host ant of the final instar larvae is also the Spotted Sugar Ant *(Camponotus maculatus)*, the larvae and pupae of which they eat. There are minor differences in the appearance of both the larvae and pupae of the two species.

48 Peninsula Blue *Lepidochrysops oreas oreas* Skitterbloutjie

WINGSPAN: About 31 mm, but much smaller individuals occur.

SEXES: Females are distinguishable from the males by the darker markings on the uppersides of their wings.

DISTRIBUTION: This brilliant blue butterfly occurs on many Peninsula mountains including the Table Mountain range. Further east it flies along the coast as far as Hermanus and Stanford.

FLIGHT PERIOD: Mainly from October until January.

FOOD PLANTS AND EARLY STAGES: The food plants of the early instar larvae and the kind of association with ants of the final instar larvae of the Peninsula Blue are the same as those of the Monkey Blue (46) and Trimen's Blue (47), but the host ant of the larvae is a Black Sugar Ant known as the Black Marsh Ant *(Camponotus niveosetosus)*.

49 Robertson's Blue *Lepidochrysops robertsoni* Robertsonbloutjie

WINGSPAN: About 30 mm, but smaller individuals are not uncommon.

SEXES: Similar.

DISTRIBUTION: Widespread in the Cape Peninsula and on many mountains in the Western Cape and far beyond. At Mamre and Strandfontein this dark species flies at sea level. It is often seen flying together with one or more of the three previously mentioned related Blues.

FLIGHT PERIOD: October to January.

FOOD PLANTS AND EARLY STAGES: The early instar larvae feed on *Selago* flowers and, like those of the Peninsula Blue (48), the final instar larvae have an obligatory and close association with the Black Marsh Ant *(Camponotus niveosetosus)*. Early spring adults of this species may possibly produce a second brood in January.

47a Trimen's Blue ♂, ♀   47b Trimen's Blue, ♂ underside

47c Trimen's Blue, larva in nest of Spotted
Sugar Ant

48a Peninsula Blue ♂, ♀   48b Peninsula Blue ♂ underside

49a Robertson's Blue
♂, ♀   49b Robertson's Blue, ♂ underside

Whites and Yellows (Pierids)

50 Cabbage White *Pieris brassicae* Koolwitjie

WINGSPAN: About 62 mm.

SEXES: Females usually larger than males and distinguishable from them by extra black dots on the wing uppersides.

DISTRIBUTION: This butterfly was introduced into South Africa from Europe. The first specimens were seen in and around Cape Town in July 1994. Since then the species has established itself throughout the Cape Peninsula and neighbouring areas, where it has become extremely common. At present its distribution appears to be restricted to more or less the Western Cape.

FLIGHT PERIOD: All year round. Adults are often seen on sunny days in midwinter. They are most prolific during spring and summer.

FOOD PLANTS AND EARLY STAGES: Eggs are laid in batches of up to 100 or more on the underside of leaves of food plants such as Cabbage, Cauliflower, Beetroot and other cruciferous cultivated crops. The larvae also feed on the introduced weed known as Wild Mustard *(Rapistrum rugosum)*, and the garden plant, Sweet Alyssum *(Lobularia maritima)*. They thrive on Nasturtiums *(Tropaeolum majus)* and on Watercress *(Rorippa nasturtium-aquaticum)*. The larvae are gregarious, especially during their early instars. Pupation occurs often well away from the larval food plants, against walls, fences and other suitable supports. Mature larvae frequently wander into houses, outhouses, sheds and other sheltered areas, where they pupate out of reach of parasitoids. Adults emerge after about two weeks in spring and early summer, but during winter many pupae hibernate. During the drier summer months from December until mid-February, many pupae estivate, giving rise to an autumn population and brood of the butterfly.

NOTE: In the Cape Peninsula many larvae are infested with larvae of parasitic flies and wasps, and very many pupae are killed by the larvae of tiny parasitic wasps. Notwithstanding these hazards, many larvae and pupae survive, as is evidenced by the many adults seen on the wing all year round. The larvae of the Cabbage White can cause considerable damage to cabbage and cauliflower crops. The Western Cape's climate, and especially the mild Peninsula weather, appears to suit the butterfly, judging by their noticeably larger size when compared with their European counterparts.

51 Meadow White *Pontia helice helice* Bontrokkie

WINGSPAN: About 40 mm.

SEXES: Easily distinguishable by their upperside markings.

DISTRIBUTION: Common everywhere in the Cape Peninsula and most of southern Africa. It is often seen in urban gardens.

FLIGHT PERIOD: All year round, even on sunny days in midwinter.

FOOD PLANTS AND EARLY STAGES: The larvae feed on various cruciferous weeds such as Hedge Mustard *(Sisymbrium officinale)*, Cape Peppercress *(Lepidium capense)*, Wild Mustard *(Rapistrum rugosum)* and Sweet Alyssum *(Lobularia maritima)*. The slender pupa is usually attached to the food plant or another nearby suitable support. The species is multi-brooded.

50a Cabbage White ♂

50b Cabbage White ♀

50c Cabbage White, ovipositing on Sweet Alyssum

50d Cabbage White, larva

50e Cabbage White, pupae

51a Meadow White, ♂, ♀

51b Meadow White, ♀ underside

51c Meadow White, larva

WHITES AND YELLOWS (Pierids)

52 Common Dotted Border *Mylothris agathina* Gewone Spikkelrandjie

WINGSPAN: About 60 mm.

SEXES: On the upperside males are mainly white, while the females are orange-yellow in colour.

DISTRIBUTION: In South Africa this butterfly was only known from the eastern parts of the country, but from about 1965 it slowly extended its range westwards. From about 1980, it was seen in the Western Cape and soon after that its distribution reached the Cape Peninsula, where it is now quite common.

FLIGHT PERIOD: All year round, but in the Peninsula is much less plentiful during the winter months.

FOOD PLANTS AND EARLY STAGES: In the Cape Peninsula, the larvae feed on Cape Sumach *(Colpoon compressum)*, which grows on the roots of other shrubs such as Wild Currant *(Rhus* spp.), to which it bears some resemblance. The females lay batches of up to 80 eggs on the leaves of this plant. The larvae are gregarious and, when not feeding, cling together in clusters. The pupae are usually attached to the food plant.

52a Common Dotted Border
♂, ♀

52b Common Dotted Border, ♂ underside

52c Common Dotted Border, ♀ underside

52d Common Dotted Border, larvae, first instar on Cape Sumach

52e Common Dotted Border, larvae, late instar

52f Common Dotted Border, pupae

53 African Clouded Yellow *Colias electo electo* Lusernvlinder

WINGSPAN: About 41 mm.

SEXES: Two female forms (see Note below).

DISTRIBUTION: Common throughout southern Africa, it is often seen in gardens.

FLIGHT PERIOD: All year round, though very scarce during midwinter.

FOOD PLANTS AND EARLY STAGES: The females oviposit on Lucerne *(Medicago sativa)*, hence the alternative name – Lucerne Butterfly – for this species. Other common larval food plants include Clover *(Trifolium* spp.) and Vetch *(Vicia* spp.).

NOTE: The African Clouded Yellow has two female forms, a common yellow form, and a greyish to bluish form that is much less common in the Cape Peninsula. Other colour varieties of both males and females are known from elsewhere in the Western Cape.

53a African Clouded Yellow, ♂

53b African Clouded Yellow, two colour forms of ♀

53c African Clouded Yellow, ♂ feeding

53d African Clouded Yellow, ♀ feeding

53e African Clouded Yellow, larva

53f African Clouded Yellow, pupa

53g African Clouded Yellow, blue ♀ underside

54 African Migrant *Catopsilia florella* Afrikaanse Swerwer

WINGSPAN: About 60 mm.

SEXES: There are four female forms (see Note below).

DISTRIBUTION: Throughout southern Africa. Before the 1970s, the African Migrant was only rarely seen in the Cape Peninsula, but from about 1976 it was found breeding here and, for a time, was quite common. However, from about 1985 its numbers began to diminish, and the insects once again became quite rare, although it was common and breeding in the summer of 1999 and in the first five months of 2000.

FLIGHT PERIOD: In the Peninsula, the butterfly is seen usually only during the summer months, well into autumn.

FOOD PLANTS AND EARLY STAGES: In the Cape Peninsula, the larvae feed on Peanut Butter Cassia or Popcorn Bush *(Senna didymobotrya)*. The larvae are green with black and yellow lines laterally. The pupae are green with a yellow stripe on each side, and blend in well with the colour of the food plant. The African Migrant is multi-brooded.

NOTE: Migratory movements of the African Migrant take place almost annually, at least on a small scale, but sometimes, probably due to population explosions of the species in some areas, major migrations occur. The African Migrant has four female forms, two of which are common in South Africa. The most common form in the Cape Peninsula is white, and resembles the male. The other, less common form, is a beautiful sulphur yellow colour. Intermediate colour forms also occur.

54a African Migrant, freshly emerged ♂

54b African Migrant, two colour forms of ♀

54c African Migrant, yellow ♀ feeding

54d African Migrant, ♀ intermediate colour form

54e African Migrant, two colour forms of larvae, feeding on Peanut Butter Cassia

54f African Migrant, pupa

Swallowtails (Papilionids)

55 Citrus Swallowtail *Papilio demodocus demodocus* Lemoenswaelstert

WINGSPAN: About 84 mm.

SEXES: Similar.

DISTRIBUTION: This, the largest of the Cape Peninsula butterflies, occurs throughout South Africa and far beyond its borders. It is particularly common in the Peninsula, and is often seen in urban gardens, where it visits the Citrus trees *(Citrus* spp.) on which the females oviposit.

FLIGHT PERIOD: Mainly during the summer months. In the Cape Peninsula, it is particularly plentiful during December and January, hence its alternative name, the Christmas Butterfly.

FOOD PLANTS AND EARLY STAGES: In the Cape Peninsula, the main larval food plants are Citrus trees, Fennel *(Foeniculum vulgare)*, Blisterbush *(Peucedanum galbanum)* and Cape Chestnut *(Calodendrum capense)*. The young larvae feeding on Citrus and Chestnut trees resemble bird droppings in colour, perhaps confusing potential predators. The early instar larvae feeding on Fennel and Blisterbush are rather plain in colour. Later instar larvae also occur in two distinct colour forms: those feeding on Citrus and Chestnut trees and related plants are nearly all of a uniform green colour with a brown to black diagonal stripe on each side, while those feeding on Fennel and Blisterbush are nearly all darker, with ill-defined markings rendering them less conspicuous on their fine-leaved food plants. The pupae vary in colour, but are generally lighter against a light background and darker in dark surroundings. Stuck against a branch or stem, a Swallowtail pupa is hardly noticeable. The Citrus Swallowtail has a succession of broods. The larvae, when plentiful, can do damage in Citrus orchards, where they are known as Orange Dogs. (See also p. 10 under Swallowtails and Swordtails).

55a Citrus Swallowtail, ♂

55b Citrus Swallowtail, freshly emerged ♀ on pupal skin

55c Citrus Swallowtail larva, fennel form with extended osmeterium

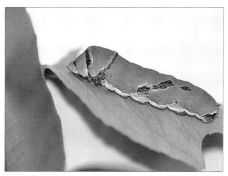

55d Citrus Swallowtail, larva, citrus form (Orange Dog)

55e Citrus Swallowtail, pupa, dark form

55f Citrus Swallowtail, pupa, light form

Skippers (Hesperids)

56 Dwarf Sandman   *Spialia nanus*   Dwergsandmannetjie

WINGSPAN: About 18 mm. Females about 24 mm.

SEXES: Similar.

DISTRIBUTION: Common in the Cape Peninsula, particularly on the lower slopes of the Table Mountain range. Predominantly a Cape species, it also penetrates the Free State.

FLIGHT PERIOD: September to May, with a few emergences also occuring on warm winter days.

FOOD PLANTS AND EARLY STAGES: The larvae feed on *Hermannia* species and a small, yellow-flowering wild Hibiscus *(Hibiscus aethiopicus)*. The larvae live concealed in shelters made on leaves of the food plant. Pupation also takes place in these shelters. The species is multi-brooded.

57 Boland Sandman   *Spialia sataspes*   Bolandsandmannetjie

WINGSPAN: Males about 24 mm, females about 27 mm.

SEXES: Similar.

DISTRIBUTION: Rarer on the Table Mountain range than it used to be, it still occurs on the slopes of hills and mountains of the Cape Peninsula and the Western Cape as a whole.

FLIGHT PERIOD: Throughout the summer months.

FOOD PLANTS AND EARLY STAGES: *Hermannia* species and wild Hibiscus *(Hibiscus aethiopicus)*. The larvae construct shelters on the leaves on which they feed and pupate. The species is multi-brooded.

58 Common Sandman   *Spialia diomus ferax*   Kwaggasandmannetjie

WINGSPAN: Males about 24 mm, females about 27 mm.

SEXES: Similar.

DISTRIBUTION: Common in the Cape Peninsula and occurring throughout southern Africa.

FLIGHT PERIOD: All year round, but very scarce during the winter months in the colder districts.

FOOD PLANTS AND EARLY STAGES: The larvae feed on *Hermannia* species and wild Hibiscus *(Hibiscus aethiopicus)*. They live concealed in leaf shelters and pupate in them. The Common Sandman is multi-brooded.

59 Mafa Sandman   *Spialia mafa mafa*   Mafasandmannetjie

WINGSPAN: Males about 19 mm, females about 24 mm.

SEXES: Similar.

DISTRIBUTION: It occurs sporadically in sandy dune habitats along the Western Cape coast far into Namaqualand. Close to Cape Town, it may be encountered just within the Cape Peninsula. It definitely occurs near the coast close to Bloubergstrand and at Melkbosstrand. Further inland it occurs at Mamre, Malmesbury and Tygerberg Hills.

FLIGHT PERIOD: Mainly from September until April or May.

FOOD PLANTS AND EARLY STAGES: The larval food plants include *Hermannia* species and wild Hibiscus *(Hibiscus aethiopicus)*. The larvae construct shelters of the leaves on which they feed, and when mature, pupate in them. The Mafa Sandman is multi-brooded.

56a Dwarf Sandman,
♂ upperside, ♀ underside

56b Dwarf Sandman, larvae on *Hibiscus aethiopicus*

57 Boland Sandman, ♂ upperside,
♀ underside

58 Common Sandman,
♂ upperside, ♀ underside

59 Mafa Sandman, ♀ upperside,
♂ underside

60 Mountain Sandman *Spialia spio* Bergsandmannetjie

WINGSPAN: Males about 24 mm, females about 27 mm.
SEXES: Similar.
DISTRIBUTION: Common in the Cape Peninsula and far beyond. It prefers lower slopes to hill tops.
FLIGHT PERIOD: All year round.
FOOD PLANTS AND EARLY STAGES: *Hermannia* species and wild Hibiscus *(Hibiscus aethiopicus)*. A female has been observed ovipositing on cultivated Hibiscus *(Hibiscus rosa-sinensis)*. The larva constructs a shelter on the leaf on which it feeds, and, upon reaching maturity, pupates in it. The Mountain Sandman is a multi-brooded species.

61 Grass-veld Sylph *Metisella malgacha malgacha* Grasveldwalsertjie

WINGSPAN: About 27 mm.
SEXES: Similar.
DISTRIBUTION: Common in the Cape Peninsula and the greater part of southern Africa. It prevails on grassy slopes, in gorges and in urban gardens.
FLIGHT PERIOD: All year round, but very scarce during the winter months in the colder districts.
FOOD PLANTS AND EARLY STAGES: The larva feeds on Shade Ehrharta *(Ehrharta erecta)*. It constructs a tube by drawing the edges of a grass blade together with silk. It eats from the top of the tube, extending it downwards as it shortens. Pupation also takes place within such a tube. It is often found breeding in urban gardens. The Grass-veld Sylph is multi-brooded.

60a Mountain Sandman, upperside

60b Mountain Sandman, ♂ underside

60c Mountain Sandman, larva

60d Mountain Sandman, pupa, imago about to emerge

61a Grass-veld Sylph, ♂ and ♀

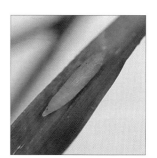

61b Grass-veld Sylph, ♀ underside   61c Grass-veld Sylph, larva   61d Grass-veld Sylph, pupa

62 Gold-spotted Sylph *Metisella metis metis* Reënwoudwalsertjie

WINGSPAN: About 38 mm.

SEXES: Similar.

DISTRIBUTION: Common in the Cape Peninsula and further east. It usually occurs near water and in damp, shady, grass-covered places.

FLIGHT PERIOD: All year round, but is very scarce during the winter months.

FOOD PLANTS AND EARLY STAGES: The larvae feed on Shade Ehrharta *(Ehrharta erecta)*, Broad-leaved Panicum *(Panicum deustum)*, Coastal Buffalo Grass *(Stenotaphrum secundatum)*, Bushmangrass *(Stipa dregeana)*, and others. Like the larva of the Grass-veld Sylph, the larva of the Gold-spotted Sylph constructs a shelter of grass blades, on which it feeds. The mature larva also pupates in this shelter. This species is multi-brooded.

63 Barber's Ranger *Kedestis barbarae bunta* Barberwagtertjie

WINGSPAN: About 26 mm.

SEXES: Females often larger than males.

DISTRIBUTION: Restricted to the Cape Peninsula, where it was once common in damp, grassy localities around the Steenberg Railway Station near Retreat, and at Strandfontein. Its habitats have mostly been destroyed, but it still occurs at Strandfontein.

FLIGHT PERIOD: September until mid-October.

FOOD PLANTS AND EARLY STAGES: The larvae feed on Cottonwool Grass *(Imperata cylindrica)* and construct a tube by drawing the edges of a grass blade together. It feeds from the tip of the tube, extending it downwards as it shortens. Pupation takes place within such a tube. The species is single-brooded.

64 Unique Ranger *Kedestes lenis* Unieke Wagtertjie

WINGSPAN: About 28 mm.

SEXES: Females usually larger than males.

DISTRIBUTION: In the Cape Peninsula, the species is confined to Strandfontein on the Cape Flats, where its existence, together with that of the Barber's Ranger, is threatened by the spread of alien vegetation and rapid urbanisation.

FLIGHT PERIOD: During November and December.

FOOD PLANTS AND EARLY STAGES: The larvae feed on Cottonwool Grass *(Imperata cylindrica)*. The early stages have not been recorded, but their behaviour and feeding habits would be similar to those of Barber's Ranger.

62a Gold-spotted Sylph, upperside

62b Gold-spotted Sylph, underside

62c Gold-spotted Sylph, larva

62d Gold-spotted Sylph, pupa

63 Barber's Ranger, ♂, ♀ and underside

64 Unique Ranger, ♂, ♀ and underside

65 Palm-tree Nightfighter *Zophopetes dysmephila* Palmskemervegter

WINGSPAN: About 38 mm.

SEXES: Differ in markings on both the upper- and undersides of the wings.

DISTRIBUTION: Widespread in the southern and eastern parts of South Africa, but known from the Cape Peninsula only since about 1980.

FLIGHT PERIOD: All year round except during the coldest winter months in the Cape Peninsula. This Skipper flies at dusk and is, therefore, rarely seen. In the evening, it is sometimes attracted to artificial light, but is then easily mistaken for a moth.

FOOD PLANTS AND EARLY STAGES: In the Cape Peninsula, the principal larval food plant is the common Wild Date Palm *(Phoenix reclinata)*. The young larva constructs a shelter by drawing the edges of the tip of a palm leaf together by means of silk. The later instar larva uses silk to pull two or three leaves together. It feeds from the top of the shelter, extending it downwards as it shortens. Pupation also takes place in such a shelter.

NOTE: The Palm-tree Nightfighter was introduced into the Cape Peninsula from the eastern parts of the country, probably on Wild Date Palms used as garden plants. After the earliest sightings in and around Cape Town in about 1980, the Skipper was soon found breeding in many places in the Peninsula. It is still fairly common here in spite of parasitoids attacking the larvae and pupae, and insectivorous birds, such as the little Cape White-eye *(Zosterops pallidus capensis)* tearing the larvae and pupae from their shelters and devouring them.

66 White-branded Swift *Pelopidas thrax inconspicua* Witmerkratsvlieër

WINGSPAN: About 38 mm.

SEXES: Similar, but females larger on average.

DISTRIBUTION: Widely distributed in South Africa, but not common, this species is localised in the Cape Peninsula. It has disappeared from some localities such as Blinkwater Gorge above Camps Bay, but it still occurs on the eastern side of Steenberg Railway Station near Retreat, where its larval food plants can be found in small patches.

FLIGHT PERIOD: Throughout the year in the Cape Peninsula, except during the coldest winter months.

FOOD PLANTS AND EARLY STAGES: In the Cape Peninsula, the larvae use Cottonwool Grass *(Imperata cylindrica)* and Shade Ehrharta *(Ehrharta erecta)*. The early instar larva lives concealed in a tube constructed from a blade of grass, but the later instar lies along a blade of grass. The pupa is either attached to grass or it is hidden in a tube of three grass blades constructed by the larva prior to pupation. The White-branded Swift is multi-brooded.

65a Palm-tree Nightfighter, ♂ and ♀ upperside

65b Palm-tree Nightfighter, ♂ and ♀ underside

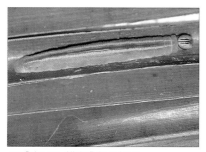

65c Palm-tree Nightfighter, larva

65d Palm-tree Nightfighter, pupa

65e Date-palm leaves eaten by larvae of the Palm-tree Nightfighter

66 White-branded Swift, ♂, ♀ and underside

67 Common Hottentot   *Gegenis niso niso*   Geelhotnot

WINGSPAN: About 27 mm.

SEXES: The females differ from males in markings on the uppersides of the wings.

DISTRIBUTION: Common in the Cape Peninsula and almost everywhere in South Africa.

FLIGHT PERIOD: All year round, but scarce during the winter months.

FOOD PLANTS AND EARLY STAGES: The larva feeds on Shade Ehrharta *(Ehrharta erecta)* and Kikuyu *(Pennisetum clandestinum)*. It conceals itself in a tube constructed from a blade of grass. Pupation occurs outside the tube, and not always on the host grass.

NOTE: The male Common Hottentot occurs in two colour forms: a brown form, and a less common yellow-ochre form. Intermediate forms also occur. There is only one female form.

67a Common Hottentot, ♂ dark form

67b Common Hottentot, ♂ light form

67c Common Hottentot, ♀

67d Common Hottentot, underside of ♂ at rest

67e Common Hottentot, larva

67f Common Hottentot, pupa

Occasional Migrants

68 Yellow Pansy *Precis hierta cebrene* Geelgesiggie

The Yellow Pansy occurs in most of South Africa, but in the Western Cape it is only found as far west as the Swellendam district. Only a few specimens have been sighted in the Cape Peninsula during this butterfly's migration, and it usually does not breed here. However, in 1986 the Yellow Pansy was found breeding in several places in and near Cape Town. The larval food plant was Bush Violet *(Barleria obtusa)*, an autumn-flowering popular garden shrublet. In that year, the Pansy produced a succession of broods, but by the end of the year no more specimens were seen. The butterfly was again seen breeding on Bush Violet in the Cape Peninsula in the early months of the year 2000.

69 Common Diadem *Hypolymnas misippus* Gewone Na-aper

This butterfly is widespread in southern Africa, but in the Western Cape it usually does not occur further west than the Swellendam district. Records from the Cape Peninsula nearly always concern males, which are easily recognisable by their striking colours. The females mimic the unpalatable African Monarch (1) and they are thus easily overlooked.

The Diadem has not been found breeding in the Peninsula. It was seen again in the Cape Peninsula in the early months of 2000.

70 Brown-veined White *Belenois aurota* Grasveldwitjie

Although widely distributed in southern Africa, the Brown-veined White avoids the extreme southwestern parts of the Western Cape. It is occasionally recorded from the Cape Peninsula, sometimes in considerable numbers, as in 1980 and again in 1984. It has not been recorded breeding in the Peninsula.

68a Yellow Pansy, ♂

68b Yellow Pansy, ♀

68c Yellow Pansy, ♀ resting on *Barleria obtusa*

69a Common Diadem, ♂

69b Common Diadem, ♀

69c Common Diadem, ♀ underside

70a Brown-veined White, ♂

70b Brown-veined White, ♀

70c Brown-veined White, ♂ underside

ACKNOWLEDGEMENTS

I acknowledge with thanks all the persons who have been directly or indirectly involved in the preparation and production of this book. However, I am most deeply indebted to the following persons.

The late Mr Charles C. G. Dickson, with whom I was privileged to enjoy 25 years of close cooperation in the study of the Cape Peninsula's butterflies. Charles was a world-renowned and celebrated lepidopterist, affectionately known by his many 'butterfly' friends as their 'Great Master'. He was also a meticulous entomological artist.

Mr Tony Brinkman, for supplying valuable locality records, for checking the early drafts of the manuscript and for the loan of set specimens used for colour photography.

Dr John Rourke, Curator of the Compton Herbarium, Kirstenbosch, for personally checking the accuracy of the scientific names of larval food plants.

Mr Alan Heath, past Chairman of the Cape Branch of the Lepidopterists' Society of Africa, for the loan of some of his excellent photographs of the early stages of ant-associated butterflies. Thanks to Alan also for sharing with me his extensive knowledge of ant association in Lycaenid butterflies.

Dr Jonathan Ball, present chairman of the Cape Branch of the Lepidopterists' Society of Africa, for his encouraging comments during the preparation of the manuscript.

Mrs E.B. Hofer for her permission to reproduce the very useful map of the Cape Peninsula, which she prepared for the 1980 publication, *Butterflies of the Table Mountain Range.*

Dr S.F. Henning, senior lecturer at Bath University, United Kingdom, for allowing me to reproduce some of his line illustrations, which will contribute to a better understanding of some of the text in the introduction.

Mr Dick Wilkins (publisher), Ms Brenda Brickman (editor) and Mrs Mandy McKay (designer), for their dedication and professionalism in ensuring a high standard of production of this book, and with whom working on this publication has been most enjoyable.

Last, but not least, I express my sincere gratitude to my wife Jill, for her forbearance, genuine interest and encouragement during the preparation of this book.

BIBLIOGRAPHY AND FURTHER READING

A plethora of information is available on butterflies, including papers on myrmecophilous relationships, breeding, parasitoids, migrations and life histories of specific lepidopteron species. Many of these valuable papers – compiled by the author of this book, as well as other butterfly specialists, including Messrs J.B. Ball, C.G.C. Dickson, A. Heath, G.C. Clark, C.B. Cottrell, D.H. Geertsema, D. Kroon, E. Pringle and G.A. and S.F. Henning – are available at various libraries.

The following is a list of the more comprehensive publications on southern African butterflies. The extensive bibliography found in Pennington's should be consulted for reference to other works on these fascinating creatures.

CLAASSENS, A.J.M. and DICKSON, C.G.C. 1980. *Butterflies of the Table Mountain Range.* Struik Publishers, Cape Town.

HENNING, G.A. and S.F., JOANNOU, J.G., WOODHALL, S.E. 1997. *Living Butterflies of Southern Africa.* Vol. 1. Hesperiidae, Papilionidae and Pieridae of South Africa. Umdaus Press, Hatfield, South Africa.

HENNING, G.A. and S.F. 1989. *South African Red Data Book: Butterflies.* SA National Scientific Programmes Report No 158. CSIR, Pretoria.

KROON, D.M. 1999. *Lepidoptera of Southern Africa. Host-plants and other associations.* Lep. Soc. of Africa and D. M. Kroon.

MIGDOLL, I. 1994. *Field Guide to the Butterflies of Southern Africa.* Struik Publishers, Cape Town.

PENNINGTON, K.M. 1994. *Pennington's Butterflies of Southern Africa.* Edited and revised by E.L.L. Pringle, G.A. Henning, J.B. Ball. Struik Winchester, Cape Town.

PINHEY, E.C.G. 1965. *Butterflies of Southern Africa.* Don Nelson, Cape Town.

SKAIFE, S.H. 1979. *African Insect Life.* Revised edition by John Ledger, photographs by Anthony Bannister. Struik Publishers, Cape Town.

VAN NOORT, S. 1999. *Sasol's First Field Guide to Butterflies and Moths of Southern Africa.* Struik Publishers, Cape Town.

WEAVING, ALAN. 2000. *Southern African Insects and their World.* Struik Publishers, Cape Town.

WILLIAMS, M.C. 1994. *Butterflies of Southern Africa: A field guide.* Southern Book Publishers, Halfway House.

WOODHALL, S.E. et al. 1992. *A Practical Guide to Butterflies and Moths in Southern Africa.* Lepidopterists' Society of Southern Africa, Florida Hills.

INDEX

to the common English and Afrikaans names, and the scientific names of butterflies of the Cape Peninsula (as numbered in this book).